Better by Bedtime

with

EFT

An Introduction to
Emotional Freedom Techniques™
by
Jean Faithful

Disclaimer

This book is intended to teach the basics of EFT for personal use. The technique is simple and easy to learn. However, you, the reader, must assume responsibility for your own emotional, physical and spiritual welfare. Please use your common sense. If in doubt it is wise to seek the help of a qualified EFT practitioner. If you have an acute or chronic health problem please consult your GP before using EFT. The author and publishers disclaim any liability arising directly or indirectly from the use of this book and take no responsibility whatsoever for your actions or the outcome of any EFT treatment administered by you, on yourself or others.

First printed November 2003
This print 2006

Published by
New Vision Media LLP

www.newvisionmedia.co.uk

© Author's copyright - Jean Faithful

ISBN 0-9549222-3-9

Design and layout by Natura Design.
NaturaDesign@aol.com

Printed and bound in the UK by T. J. International
Padstow, Cornwall

Acknowledgements

I would like to thank Gary Craig for the wonderful gift he has given to us all, and for his dedication and commitment to spreading the word of EFT; Tom, for her total support and belief in me; Jamie, for his instruction, assistance and his patience and kindness to me, a 'friend of a friend', Sue, Shelley, Sue and Isy for their feedback; and all my friends, family and colleagues who were prepared to trust in me and be guinea pigs when I first started to study EFT. I will be eternally grateful for their willingness to put up with me and my evangelical zeal!

Contents

1   My Own Story

7   Beyond Belief?

17   What is EFT?

27   Explanation of Points

39   The Sequence

51   Clearing the Obstacles

63   Physical Pain

67   Fear and Phobias

75   Stress

85   Trauma

91   EFT and Children

99   Case Histories

130   Afterword

132   Addendum

Chapter One

My Own Story

"...whatsoever ye shall ask in prayer,
believing, ye shall receive."
Matthew 21:22

One day, during a 'heart to heart' with a friend I heard myself say *"Of course, being miserable is part of my persona these days"*. I was shocked to the core to hear these words come out of my mouth. I drove home with my words running around and around my head.

When I got home I had a good look at myself. I have always considered myself to be an optimistic, positive, 'glass half full' sort of person; and the person I saw now was not me. Little by little, over the last, stressful few years, I had changed and I was no longer who I am.

I was very aware of what my big issue was. My mother had died two years ago and my grief was getting heavier, not better. She had spent the last four years of her life in a nursing home, which I knew I carried guilt for. I also felt especially bereft that I was now an 'orphan', (even though I am a grown woman!) I had tried, but I couldn't move the weight of my grief.

When my father died it had been very painful for me, especially as my mother was in the nursing home at the time and was not fully aware. But my grief seemed to follow a 'natural' path.

My mother died two years later. My grief did not seem to follow a 'natural' path, and the pain of my father's loss had also come back. I kept thinking it would get better, but it hadn't. So many things reminded me of them, and every one of them overwhelmed me with powerful, painful emotions and reduced me to tears.

I knew this was why I had changed and I realised that I had to do something, and fast, before the person I was becoming totally swamped the person I am. I didn't know what to do. I felt totally helpless. I closed my eyes and asked for help.

The very next day I heard about this new therapy, EFT. It sounded too good to be true, but if it worked it was just what I needed. It used meridians and balance, which fall within my belief system, (I practice reflexology and reiki), it had come into my path just when I was in need, and it could also be self administered. I decided to send away for the course and learn how to do it.

The first thing I tried it on was an acute arthritic pain in the lower joint of my thumb, which I get from time to time. Usually, when this happens, I take cod liver oil for a few days until the pain goes, but I had run out. I tried EFT. Instant relief after just one round. I poked and prodded where the pain should have been and it just wasn't there any more! It had taken about a minute to relieve a pain that had been troubling me for days!

During these difficult, past few years, I had developed the habit of scratching the palms of my hands. I had tried all sorts of strategies to stop, but I couldn't break the itch - scratch - itch cycle. I used to scratch until the skin was raw, but still I could obtain no relief. I set about using EFT on this problem, working on both the itch and the desire to scratch. Again it worked! I got really excited. I tried it out on various minor aches and pains in the family and among my friends with great success.

Fuelled by these successes, I was ready to try it out on an emotional level. I have always been scared of heights, so it seemed a good place to start. I worked on all the feelings I get associated with heights and tapped them all away. I went out and tested myself by going to places that I knew I couldn't have gone to before and experienced no discomfort at all.

I decided I had enough faith in this therapy now to deal with my 'biggie'. I would try EFT on my feelings around Mum and Dad.

Because I did not know how I would react, I asked a close friend to be with me. I worked on all the negative emotions I felt around their deaths.

There was guilt, shame, fear, anger, pain and loss; all churning around in this dark, miserable hole inside me, and in just three sessions, EFT enabled me to release them all, one by one. I freed myself from that dreadful place with EFT.

A real bonus was an unexpected side effect of the process. Since my father had died, I could not recall the emotion of my happy memories. I remembered the facts of my memories. I could remember that we had had some wonderful times, but the memories were empty without the emotions that went along with them. They were distant and misty.

One evening, I was having dinner with friends and the conversation turned to wedding dresses. I started to tell of an occasion from my childhood when my mother had cut up and dyed her treasured wedding dress because we could not afford to buy the pink satin and lace needed to produce an outfit for my school play.

As a child, I had been really upset when I found out what she had done, because she had been very sentimental about her wedding dress. But I knew that my mum must love me very much to do that for me. Once again I was overwhelmed with powerful emotions and reduced to tears.

My friends were sorry that I was getting upset again. It took a minute or two before I could speak; to tell them that this time the tears were from the joy of recognising that I was feeling my memories again. I could feel my mother's love. A wonderful moment for me, and one that I will never forget.

Now I remember my parents with fondness and love and laughter. I was very lucky to have them for so much of my life. I still miss them and on occasions I feel very sad. This is to be expected. It is 'normal'. I am me again.

Since these first experiences, I use EFT on everything. Before EFT, my fear of heights prevented me from viewing Paris from the Eiffel Tower. Heights are no longer a problem. Spiders? No problem any more. I have looked back over past, hurtful, emotional experiences and tapped them away.

Now, if I develop a headache, I tap for it. If I have been doing physical work and my muscles are aching, I tap for it. If I have been hunched over a keyboard and my shoulders are tense, I tap for it. If my breathing is congested, I tap for it. If I am feeling anxious or angry about something or somebody, I tap for it. If I lack motivation, I tap for it. Negative thoughts? Gone in a flash, thanks to EFT.

Chapter Two

Beyond Belief?

"I would rather have a mind opened by wonder than one closed by belief".
Gerry Spence, US Attorney

The human body is beautifully designed. Without any conscious effort, it takes what it needs from the air that we breathe and the food that we eat, sends it to the tissues that need it and expels what is not needed. It is designed so that we can experience the world we live in, via the five senses. It also protects us from harming ourselves.

Put your hand on a hot iron and you will remove it immediately. This is because a message is instantly transmitted along neural pathways to your brain, and a return message from the brain triggers a reflex action, which causes you to remove your hand from the source of the problem.

All faster than you can say 'Jack Flash', and all without any conscious thought or effort on your part!

The fact that our bodies do this without any conscious thought from us is taken for granted. It is also taken for granted that we don't have to consciously instruct every single muscle and joint which is involved in the very complicated processes which allow us to stand upright, and to hop, skip and jump at will. We merely think what it is we want to do (send a message), and our body's autonomous systems take over.

Amazing feats, yet we don't even give them a second thought!

These messages are electrically transmitted. The body is full of electricity. Sometimes when you undress, you can see the sparks produced by the discharge of static electricity. If our bodies didn't contain electricity, this wouldn't be possible. This electricity can be measured by electro-encephalographs, (EEGs) which record the electrical activity of the brain and electro-cardiographs, (ECGs) which record the electrical activity of the heart.

Without this continuous flow of electrically transmitted messages, we would be unable to see, hear, feel, taste or smell. We would be unable to digest our food. We would be unable to move. We would be unable to breathe. We die when this energy stops flowing.

In the Western world, medical practice concentrates on the physical and chemical make-up of the human body and largely ignores the electrical aspect of it. We visit the doctor when we feel unwell and present him with a list of symptoms. The doctor then treats these symptoms according to Western practices, based on an extensive knowledge of the body's physical anatomy and physiology, and on careful studies of the effects drugs and/or surgery have on the given ailment. Their tactics are often very successful. However, occasionally, what causes the symptoms is unknown and therefore untreated.

Thousands of years ago, the Chinese mapped out a complex system of energy circuits that run throughout the body. These energy circuits are the centre-piece of Eastern health philosophy and practice.

The aim of Eastern practitioners is to work with the body's natural inclination to heal itself. It is based on a totally different belief system from that in the West - that the human body runs on energy, or 'chi', and that this chi runs throughout the body via energy circuits; or meridians as they are called.

Over the centuries, they learned how these energy circuits affected the body and discovered that keeping this energy flowing freely is vital to health and well-being. The body is treated as a whole, and the belief that an emotional problem can weaken the body's natural defences, in the same manner as an invading bacteria or virus can, is totally accepted.

The Chinese visit their acupuncturist regularly for a check-up, and any imbalances are corrected with the use of needles inserted into the appropriate acupuncture point(s). This philosophy maintains balance and health, and, in days past, if the acupuncturist didn't do his job properly and the patient fell ill, well, he just didn't get paid!

No-one disputes the model of the body as we know it. There are tests that show what constitutes the chemical make-up of the body, and diagrams in any anatomy book show the physical make-up. And anyway, we all know we have blood in our veins because most of us, if not all, have seen it!

But we cannot say the same about meridians. You can find diagrams thousands of years old mapping out these meridians, but here in the West, no, we can't see them, so therefore we believe that they do not exist.

Let me ask you a question. If you can't see, hear, feel, taste or smell something does that mean it doesn't exist? "Of course," I hear you say, "We have five senses that show us the realities of our world. If none of them can sense anything, then it cannot exist!"

Yet love exists and I have yet to see it, or hold it within my hands and smell or taste it, and I certainly haven't heard it singing as it goes about its business!

But no-one disputes the existence of love. Nor have I experienced any of these things with somebody's soul, yet although there is great discussion as to where in the body the soul is actually situated, few people dispute the fact that it does exist somewhere in there.

The human body is a seething mass of electrical circuits and I believe that when trauma happens, we are literally shocked, electrically shocked. This is the emotional 'kick' we feel.

We are all aware that physical sensations can be induced by an external event. Many of us will have felt physical pain at the loss of a loved one, or on hearing bad news. We don't like it, but we don't think of it as weird as we have an identifiable reason for why we feel this pain. We know what triggered it, therefore we find it understandable. It hurts, but we know that it will fade with the passage of time.

Our systems get to work and send out the 'repair kit' to smooth out the wiring and put the body back into balance once more. This is the normal pattern for traumatic events in our lives.

But for a few people, this is not the case. For some reason they do not revert to balance and a negative emotional response can be triggered by a sight, or smell, connected to the previous traumatic event, or by intrusive thoughts and flashbacks of the event.

This happens beyond their conscious control. This can cause phobias and, in extreme cases, PTSD (Post Traumatic Stress Disorder) The system has broken down and needs help uncrossing its wires. EFT was designed by Gary H Craig to give this help, and this book was written to bring EFT to you.

The driving force behind EFT is the "Discovery Statement" which states, quite plainly:

"THE CAUSE OF ALL NEGATIVE EMOTIONS IS A DISRUPTION OF THE BODY'S ENERGY SYSTEM"

A very believable statement when you spend some time thinking about it. After all, spiders are not frightening monsters out to get us. A tall building is not inviting us to throw ourselves over the edge.

Yet take a random group of people and it is more than likely there will be among them those who are frightened by spiders, and those who are scared of heights. It would also be fair to say that some of these people would probably describe their fear as a phobia, and will suffer various physical symptoms, i.e. rapidly beating heart, sweating palms, anxiety, panic, hysteria etc., because of it.

In this same group of people there will be those who take spiders and heights in their stride and feel none of these sensations. Same spiders. Same tall buildings. Different reaction.

So does it not make perfect sense that it is not the spiders or the tall buildings which cause the negative reaction, but something else? Something which is "switched on" (or off) by our proximity to these things?

It is my belief that as well as taking care of our physical needs, the body is also designed to take care of our emotional health.

There are all sorts of systems built into the body's design to keep us physically nourished and healthy, ward off germs, repair damaged tissue, and keep us from harming ourselves. Is it so hard to believe that the design also includes a system to keep us emotionally healthy?

When you think about it, as our emotions are very much a part of us, it would be silly to think that a body designed so beautifully to maintain and care for us wouldn't have some little piece in there somewhere that took care of this function.

Think about it. Is there anything at all that your body doesn't do for you that you really need it to? So why not emotionally? Makes good sense really, doesn't it?

But, what if this system breaks down?

Emotional breakdown can have devastating and self-limiting effects on our lives. Some people are in therapy for years, often taking prescribed drugs as well. Some can't afford the therapy they feel they need and embark on a path of self-help, looking for a cure. Others just soldier on, with the ever present shadow of emotional pain colouring their lives.

EFT can change this, believe me.

For the time it takes to read this book, take a step beyond your beliefs and explore mine. Leave yours behind for a while and collect them up later (if you still want to!). Open your mind to the possibility that these meridian things do, in fact, exist.

To the possibility that this EFT stuff might just do 'exactly what it says on the tin'. To the possibility of being 'Better by Bedtime'.

Come with me on a journey of discovery. Try it for yourself. Test your results. I am confident you will not be disappointed!

Chapter Three

What Is EFT?

'There are no miracles, only unknown laws"
Saint Augustine AD 354-430

EFT is a painless, elegant, energy therapy, which takes only minutes to perform and its remedies are usually permanent. The treatment involves gently tapping with the fingertips on meridian points where they appear close to the body's surface.

How can this be? How can tapping with your fingertips produce such deep and profound healing in a matter of MINUTES? How can the emotional intensity of a memory change?

"It's impossible!" comes the cry "I have a terrible memory that that has kept me awake for years. There is no way you can just wipe out that pain". Well, with EFT it **is** possible and you **can** erase the pain.

EFT can access a memory, kept deeply buried so that we don't have to experience the emotional intensity that comes along with it, and change it into something that we are able to think or talk about with as little emotional impact as if we were talking about a shopping trip to Tesco!

EFT is painless in its application and rapid in its remedies.

- There is no re-living of past traumatic events

- There is no telling of painful memories

- There is no will power required

- There is no daily medication

- There is no diet sheet

- There is no strict exercise regime

There is just a simple procedure that takes merely minutes to perform. This rapid technique relieves you of your emotional baggage, usually permanently, and frees you to go about your life more effectively.

EFT flies in the face of just about every belief there is about psychology and emotional healing. Yet, time after time, people come to me, sometimes so deeply distressed that they are unable even to utter the words to describe their pain. They are heavy with emotional pain, overwhelmed by guilt or shame or anxiety or fear.

And, time after time, after a session with EFT, I see these people leave with a smile on their face and a lighter heart, with the pain of their emotional intensity tapped away.

EFT, with its elegant simplicity, can change your life. It can give you the ability to live your life free from negative emotions such as self-doubt... or anger... or grief over the loss of a loved one... or negative memories involving rape or other forms of abuse. EFT gives you freedom.

Freedom from the anxiety that causes you to take those pills, drink that alcohol, smoke those cigarettes or raid the 'fridge. Freedom from intense fears... or phobias... or constant "stress" headaches ... or anxiety... or PTSD... or addictive cravings... or... or............ the list goes on and on. Freedom, as you can see, to dramatically change your world!

EFT has been successful in treating the following problems, often showing results in minutes:

- Addictions
- Alcoholism
- Anxiety
- Asthma
- Constipation
- Panic Attacks

- Grief
- Insomnia
- Physical pain
- Fear of public speaking
- Toothache
- PMT
- Negative thoughts and feelings
- Fears and phobias such as:

    * Flying

    * Lifts

    * Heights

    * Spiders

    * Claustrophobia/agoraphobia

    * Dentists

    * Snakes

    * Mice

    * Water

    * Rejection

All these and many, many more have been successfully treated with EFT.

This is because EFT goes straight to the cause of the problem. The cause of negative emotions is not the memories of the emotionally painful events. The cause of negative emotions is not the intrusive thoughts of the emotionally painful events.

Remember the discovery statement?

"The cause of all negative emotions is a disruption of the body's energy system"

This is the essence of EFT. The theory behind this discovery statement is amazingly simple. It is a totally new concept. Allow me to let the master explain it to you himself. I make no apologies for quoting Gary Craig at length here, because it is important that you understand the concept behind EFT, and nobody does it better than Gary.

First, notice what the discovery statement does not say. It does not say that a negative emotion is caused by the memory of a past traumatic event. This is important to recognise because that presumed connection of traumatic memories to negative emotions is a mainstay in conventional psychotherapy. In some circles, it is the accepted practice to "treat the memory" and, in the process, ask the client to repeatedly re-live some emotionally painful event. EFT, by contrast, respects the memory but addresses the true cause...a disruption in the body's energy system. People call me from all over the country for help over the telephone. Without my asking, they invariably start telling me in detail about their past traumas.

That's because they mistakenly believe I need all these details to help them. To them these memories are the cause of their problems. I care deeply about helping people who needlessly carry around all these emotionally charged memories.

But it always seems strange to people when I tell them they don't need to painfully re-live all these horrid details for EFT to help them. These memories may contribute to an unwanted emotion, but they are not the direct cause. Accordingly, we don't need to spend time painfully dwelling on them. It is superfluous to do so.

21

Thus there is very little emotional suffering with EFT. It is relatively painless. You will be asked to briefly recall your problem (there may be some discomfort in that), but that is all. There is no need to relive the pain. In fact, with EFT, generating prolonged emotional discomfort is frowned upon. This is but one example of where EFT is a radical departure from conventional methods. It might help if you compare the energy flow in your body to that of a TV set. As long as the electricity flows through your TV normally, the sound and picture are both clear. But what would happen if you took off the back of the TV set and poked a screwdriver amongst all that "electrical spaghetti"? You would, quite obviously, disrupt or re-route the flow of electricity and an electrical "zzzzt" would occur inside. The picture and sound would become erratic and the TV would exhibit its version of a "negative emotion"

In the same manner, when our energy systems become unbalanced, we have an electrical "zzzzt" effect going on inside. Straighten out this "zzzzt" and the negative emotion goes away. It's that simple. I'm well aware how strange this may sound and how difficult it can be to believe...at least at first. I wouldn't believe it myself if I hadn't seen such marvelous changes in people after applying these techniques.

The intermediate step...the missing piece. Once you accept it, though...once you "let it in"...its logic becomes obvious and you begin to see all the weaknesses in the other methods.

For example, the "treat the memory" method mentioned above becomes glaringly erroneous in the light of these discoveries. It is assumed, in that method, that the past traumatic memory is the direct cause of the emotional upset in someone. It is not. There is an intermediate step...a missing piece... between the memory and the emotional upset. And that intermediate step, of course, is the disruption in the body's energy system. It is that disruption, the "zzzzt", that is the direct cause of the emotional upset.

Step 1   The distressing memory
Step 2   A disruption in the body's energy system
Step 3   Negative emotion

If the memory does not cause a disruption in the body's energy system then the negative emotion cannot occur. That is why some people are bothered by their memories and others are not. The difference is that some people have a tendency for their energy systems to become inbalanced under such a memory, while others do not.

This is why some people tend to get worse when conventional psychology aims for the memory and not its cause (the energy disruption) Addressing step 1 by requiring somebody to vividly re-live a distressing memory serves to induce more disruption in the energy system. And that means more pain, not less. It can, and often does, aggravate the problem. If step 2 was addressed instead of step 1, then there would be relatively little pain. The energy system would be balanced by appropriate tapping) and internal calm would replace the negative emotion. The result would be rapid relief because the true cause was being addressed.

© 1995-2002 Gary H Craig

That is the theory behind EFT. A very simple concept. Aren't all the best ideas so simple that you find yourself wondering why no-one ever thought of them before?

Remember Gary's Discovery Statement? He is very bold. He doesn't pussyfoot around and say the cause of some negative emotions 'might perhaps' be a disruption in the body's energy system. He 'boldly goes where no man has gone before' and states quite clearly and categorically

"The cause of *ALL* negative emotions *IS* a disruption in the body's energy system"

Applying EFT to a problem attacks the true cause. If you have a height phobia, ridding yourself of your phobia means you will, in future, approach the edge of a sheer drop with the natural caution every sensible person would use. It does not mean you are going to stand with your feet halfway off the edge of it!

EFT removes a phobic ('abnormal') response, but leaves natural ('normal') caution well alone.

Nobody really knows how EFT works. All we have are theories. It is human nature to want to know how things work. It is Mankind's quest for knowledge, the desire for our questions to be answered, which raises us above other species.

Probably many times throughout this book you will have such thoughts as "How can that be?" or "I wonder how that happens?" These questions pop into my head as well.

I can't give you the 'whys' and 'wherefores' of how EFT works. I simply don't know. I have my belief that our bodies are capable of healing themselves; EFT facilitates this and allows profound healing, but I don't know how.

But long before scientists proved that dock leaves are rich in natural anti-histamines, they were being used to ease the itching rash caused by nettle stings; and willow bark was used as a cure for headaches long before it was proved that it was a naturally occurring form of analgesia.

The medicine women of days gone by weren't aware of these facts. Their belief system accepted that nature provided, and nature *did* provide. They learned that this herb or that plant cured this sickness or that ailment. In the same way that I know that EFT works, they knew that their plants and potions worked. Hundreds of years passed before science *proved* that these things did, in fact, work.

For all those years, before the scientists discovered the reasons why they worked, people were being helped all over the world. It didn't stop the healing properties of the plants from working just because the science was unknown.

So it is with EFT. **EFT works.** Not knowing the science doesn't alter that fact. EFT is in its very early days but its growth has been rapid. Interest is spreading, and all over the world, medical professionals and therapists from all disciplines are discovering it.

Discovering the impressive range of its healing potential. Experiencing its healing power, both for themselves and for their clients. Experimenting, researching and sharing their experiences and insights with each other.

One day, science will catch up and give us an explanation as to how EFT works. Why wait?

Chapter Four

Explanation of Points

"They can conquer who believe they can".
Virgil (70 BC - 19 BC)

In the following chapter the technique itself is explained, step by step. To prepare you for this, and to ensure that you gain maximum benefit from the process, this chapter is devoted to familiarising you with all the points on the body that you are going to be tapping.

Read it carefully. If you become familiar with these points, you will be able to run smoothly through the technique without having to keep turning back over the pages to see whereabouts they are.

All of these points are located where the meridians appear close to the surface of the skin and, with the exception of the ones under your nose and on your chin, are bi-lateral. This means they appear on both sides of your body and you can tap whichever side you choose. It is such a user-friendly technique that you can change from side to side throughout the process, should you so wish, with no detrimental effect. You might find that some of these tapping points feel slightly different from the areas around them. Or you might not. Either way is fine.

The 'Sore' Spots

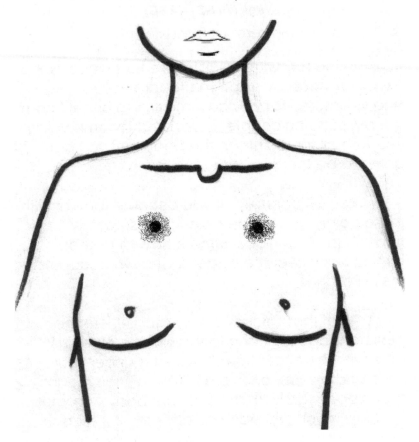

Figure 1
The 'Sore' spots

At the base of your throat there is a 'U' shape in the top of your sternum (breastbone). About three inches down and three inches to the side (which-ever side you choose) of this 'U', you will find a small area which, if you press hard on it with your fingertips, will feel tender compared with the areas around it.

This is not a large area, probably about the size of a 50p piece. Experiment until you find the right spot. Poke around firmly with the tips of your fingers until you locate it. Practise on both sides and use the side that feels right for you. When applying the technique, this area is rubbed gently in small circular motions with the pads of your fingers.

Points on the face

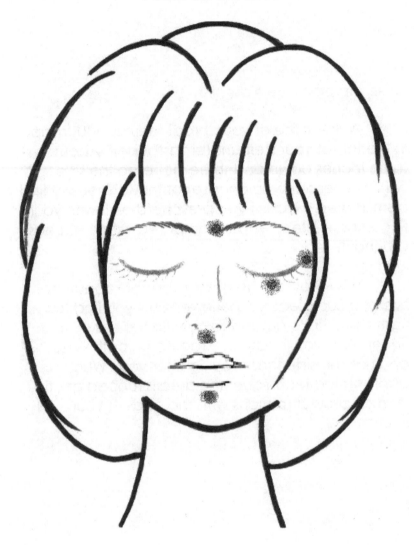

Figure 2
Points on the face

There are five tapping points on the face. These are positioned as follows:

1. At the inside edge of the eyebrow. With your fingers together, place the tips of your index, middle and ring fingers of either hand on your face, between, and in line with, your eyebrows. The tips of your index finger and ring finger are now touching the correct points to be used. Use either one of these points when applying the technique.

2. At the outside of the eye, on the bone, close to and level with the corner of the eye.

3. Underneath the eye, on the bone, beneath where the pupil is when you are looking straight ahead.

4. On the centre of the small area between the nose and the upper lip.

5. Midway between the lower lip and the point of the chin.

Points on the Torso

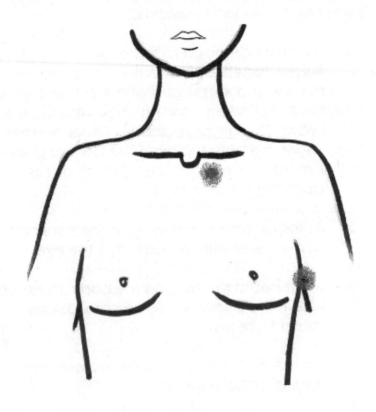

Figure 3
Points on the torso

There are two points on the upper torso.

The first is where the clavicle (collarbone), sternum (breast bone) and first rib meet. The way to find this point is to locate the 'U' shape in the centre of the top of your breastbone again, and about an inch down and an inch to the right (or left) of the 'U'.

The second is underneath the arm. It is about four inches below the armpit, roughly in line with the nipple, and will feel more tender than the area surrounding it. This is another point you may have to poke about to find, but having already found the sore spots on your chest, you should know what to expect!

Points on the hands

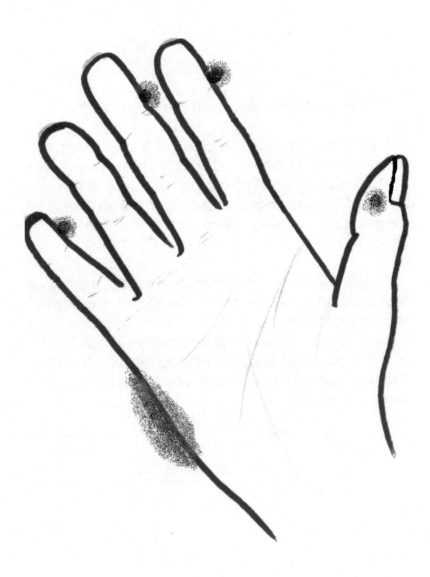

Figure 4
Points on the hands

There are also five tapping points on the hands.

1. On the thumb, level with the base of the nail on the outside edge.

2. On the index finger, level with the base of the nail on the side of the finger nearest the thumb.

3. On the middle finger, level with the base of the nail on the side of the finger nearest the index finger.

4. On the little finger level with the base of the nail on the side of the finger nearest the ring finger.

5. The karate chop point, which, as the name suggests, can be found on the fleshy part of the hand, halfway between the little finger and the wrist.

The Gamut point

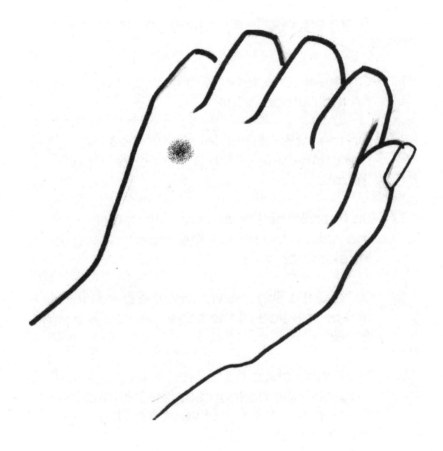

Figure 5
The Gamut Point

Lastly, we come to the point called the Gamut Point. Although this is also found on the hand, to save confusion I have not included it with the other points of the hand. Its use comes after the first round of tapping and before the second, so I have listed it separately.

Form your hand into a fist, with the back of the hand towards you. Now, imagine that the knuckles of your ring and little finger are the corners of a triangle which has equal sides. You will find the Gamut point on the back of your hand, where the third corner of this imaginary triangle would be.

Familiarise yourself with these points. Play around with them for a while until you feel you are confident enough of their positions not to have to keep checking back when you first practise the technique.

When applying EFT, these points are tapped with the fingertips. Use two or three fingertips together and tap each point about 7 times. Tap at a speed which feels comfortable. Tap firmly, with enough force to feel it, but not enough to bruise yourself. We are sorting out problems here, not adding to them!

When you are confident that you know where they all are, you are ready to begin; but before we go any further, choose for yourself a familiar tune, such as Jingle Bells or Happy Birthday, which I will be asking you to hum.

Curious? Read on!

Chapter Five

The Sequence

"Learning is not compulsory... neither is survival".
W. Edwards Deming (1900 - 1993)

Now we come to the technique itself. Find somewhere quiet and comfortable. Maybe light a candle and play some relaxing music. Take the time to read this chapter all the way through before you try EFT on your chosen issue.

Remember, you are being introduced to a new friend who will be there to help and support you for the rest of your life, so this is a big event. You are about to experience something which has the power to dramatically change your life, yet is so simple it can be learned in minutes!

A complete sequence of EFT consists of:

- The set up
- The first round of tapping
- The 9 point Gamut procedure
- The second round of tapping
- The assessment

The Set-Up

When you are settled, identify the issue you want to work on. Don't be too ambitious. Time enough for more complex issues when you have finished this book and are more familiar with the technique.

This is the first time you are going to use it, so take your time. Use pen and paper to jot down a few ideas and then select something straight-forward for your first experience, such as an anger which has a specific cause that you can easily identify.

You now need to formulate a statement which best describes your issue. This is a very important stage in the technique. Use words that are familiar to you, which you use when you think about the problem. Be honest. Be specific. If you are choosing to work with anger, instead of using 'I feel angry', direct your phrase at the particular anger you are feeling, such as:

"I feel angry that Jenny broke her promise"

"I feel angry with Dad for not letting me go to the party"

"I feel so angry with John for letting me down".

For this reason, you now give your issue a score of zero to 10 on the Subjective Units of Distress Scale (SUDS). Read through your statement and focus on how you are feeling about it right now.

Concentrate on how you are feeling. Focus on the signs that tell you that you are angry (these could be butterflies in the tummy, dry mouth, sweaty hands, whatever your own particular signs are).

Give those feelings a score from zero to 10, with 10 being the most intense feeling you could have and zero being no intensity at all. This is a subjective score, so don't worry that others may feel this issue is no big deal and yet you feel that a '10' doesn't go anywhere *near* scoring how bad you feel. It's *your* feelings we are dealing with here, not theirs. It's not a competition, it's a healing process, so if a 10 is what it feels like to you, then a 10 is the score you give it. Write this down beside your statement.

Now, focusing on your issue, rub your 'sore spot' and at the same time repeat your Set-up Statement out loud, three times. Don't be half hearted about it. Say it aloud and say it with confidence.

That completes the set up.

EFT calls for two rounds of tapping, one round before and one round after what is called the 9 Point Gamut. In the previous chapter, we mapped out the points to be tapped. The order in which you tap these points is very simple.

An easy way to remember the order is to place your hand, thumb uppermost, on your tummy. When you are in this position, each point appears below the previous one. You just start at the top and work your way down!

Remember to stay focused on your issue for the whole of the time. This is a very important part of the technique.

First Round of Tapping

Focusing on your issue, tap seven times on each of the points in the order shown, and repeat your reminder phrase aloud at each point. Tap at a speed and pressure that feels comfortable for you. Don't worry too much that you have only tapped five or six times, or maybe eight or nine times. EFT is very user friendly. It is more important to remain focused on your issue. If you tap each point whilst, and a couple of times after, saying your reminder phrase, that will be fine.

- The eyebrow

- The outer corner of your eye

- Underneath your eye

- Underneath your nose

- Your chin

- Your collarbone

- Under your arm

- Your thumb

- Your index finger

- Your middle finger

- Your little finger

- The karate point

That completes the first round of tapping.

The 9 Point Gamut

This is where the fun comes in! The 9 Point Gamut actively engages the unconscious mind in the process.

The eye movements replicate the actions of the eyes when dreaming occurs during Rapid Eye Movement (REM) sleep. REM sleep is when the brain sifts and sorts and stores all the information it has received during the day.

The humming and the counting bring both sides of the brain, the right hand creative side and the left hand logical side, into the proceedings.

Still focusing on your issue, tap the Gamut point and perform the following actions. You need to keep your head perfectly still whilst doing this.

1. Close your eyes
2. Open your eyes
3. Look hard down to the right
4. Look hard down to the left
5. Roll your eyes round clockwise
6. Roll your eyes round anti-clockwise
7. Hum a line of a familiar tune. e.g. 'Happy Birthday' or 'Jingle Bells'
8. Count 1 2 3 4 5 out loud
9. Hum a line of the tune again

That completes the 9 Point Gamut procedure.

Second Round of Tapping

Now go through one more round of the tapping sequence, from your eyebrow through to the karate point, exactly as you did before, remembering to stay focused on your issue by repeating your reminder phrase at each point.

- The eyebrow
- The outer corner of your eye
- Underneath your eye
- Underneath your nose
- Your chin
- Your collarbone
- Under your arm
- Your thumb
- Your index finger
- Your middle finger
- Your little finger
- The karate point

That completes the second round of tapping. And that's it! Yes, really!

Congratulations! You have just completed your first round of EFT!

Assessment

Now we must measure the result. This is a vital part of the proceedings. We need to test the results. Focus on your problem, and once more give it a score. If all is going according to plan, this will be lower that the original one which you wrote down.

Maybe you've moved down two or three points, maybe more. Maybe you have gone right down to a zero! Don't be disappointed if you haven't gone down to a zero yet, remember this is your first attempt and very few people become proficient at anything at their very first try.

But we want your SUDS score to be zero and so, as Gary Craig would say, "Be persistent!" Go through the procedure again but this time, adjust your set-up statement and reminder phrase to suit the new circumstances.

Remember, what you are looking for is a true statement of the problem as it is **now**, and this is now a lesser problem than it was when you started. The statements and reminder phrases must be adjusted to take this into account.

Using our previous examples these would now be:

"Even though I **still** feel **some** of this anger towards Jenny for breaking her promise I deeply and completely accept myself".

"Even though I **still** feel **some** of this anger towards Dad for not letting me go to the party, I deeply and completely accept myself".

"Even though I **still** feel **some** of this anger towards John for letting me down, I deeply and completely accept myself".

with the reminder phrase changing to 'This **remaining** anger' for all three examples. Use these statements and reminder phrases for the second and any subsequent rounds that are necessary.

Test your score after each complete application of EFT. Adjust your set up statement to suit. If you are working on anger and you realise that you are now feeling more irritated than angry, change your statement to suit the new emotion and keep going.

Even if you have to do it six times, it will still take much less than an hour. As long as you are lowering your SUDS score each time, keep going until it reaches zero.

Chapter Six

Clearing the Obstacles to Healing Success

"If at first you don't succeed, try, try, try again"
Old English Proverb

If you have had less success than you hoped for, read on, because this chapter is concerned with dealing with obstructions to healing. If you are specific with your set-up statement and persistent in your efforts, EFT will be successful in practically every case.

As this is a comparatively new therapy there are no formal statistics to back up this statement; but my own experiences, and those of my clients, as well as the many case histories and testimonials posted on Gary Craig's website by professional therapists, medical doctors and psychiatrists from all over the world; continually reinforce my belief in the healing power of EFT.

So please, don't give up. Remember that this is the first time you have tried EFT. Think of what you have learned so far as the keys on a piano. When you start to play the piano, you begin with learning what sounds the keys make. You can learn quite quickly how to play 'Chopsticks' perfectly. But you need to persevere if you want to play Beethoven or Brahms!

So it is with EFT. So far, you have learned where the notes are. You can play 'Chopsticks' proficiently. This much alone is enough to effect profound healing with straightforward issues. To work with problems that are more complex, you need to persevere. Luckily, this is a much faster process with EFT than it is with the piano!

There are a few possible reasons why EFT might seem less than 100% effective.

Psychological Reversal

Psychological Reversal, (PR), is the name given to the phenomenon that prevents us doing things we really want to do; the 'but' in "I would do it but...." and the 'because' in "I can't do that because...". I call them 'Afterthoughts'

Afterthoughts are the phrases we use in our heads to convince ourselves we can't do something, no matter how much we want to. So we give up, often before we even try.

This is negative thinking in action, working against our conscious desire to change. Often we are not even aware of these afterthoughts and we can be totally unaware of the effect they are having on our day to day lives.

No matter how much we want to change or how strong our will power may be, if we are psychologically reversed, change is impossible.

"I want to give up alcohol (*but I'm afraid I won't sleep without a drink*)"

The afterthought pops in; the subconscious listens to the inner dialogue, decides that the fear of not sleeping is a greater problem than the alcohol, and the healing process is sabotaged. Our subconscious mind is working against our conscious desire to change. It is protecting us from our fear.

Similarly, if you are trying to lose weight, your thoughts might follow along the lines of:

"I want to lose weight (*but I'm afraid I might fail*)"

The failure is something we don't want to experience, so the sub-conscious mind steps in to protect us from failure by sabotaging our slimming regime. Willpower alone is no match for negative thinking. PR, if it is present, stops any healing process dead in its tracks, not just EFT.

This is why we perform the set-up at the start of each sequence. The set-up is built into the EFT sequence to take care of PR and allow EFT to get to work on the problem. So, if you are not getting the movement you desire with EFT, listen to what you say to yourself in your head and be more specific with your set-up statements. In the previous examples, you would apply EFT using the after-thoughts as a set-up statement.

"Even though I'm afraid I won't sleep if I stop drinking, I deeply and completely accept myself".

"Even though I'm afraid I might fail in my diet, I deeply and completely accept myself".

It is always well worth hunting out your after-thoughts. They are often part of our acquired belief system; something we witnessed, experienced or were told, which our subconscious registered as a truth without our conscious mind ever questioning it.

Afterthoughts stop you moving forward and achieving your aims. They are, in fact, another aspect of your issue to be dealt with.

Aspects

Aspects are different parts of the same overall problem and each aspect should have EFT applied to it until your score has collapsed to zero.

The flying phobias in the next chapter demonstrate vividly how a problem can have a huge number of aspects. Some of these aspects will have a high score, while others may score lower.

Don't be put off. Turn detective and track down every aspect you can think of and apply EFT to each one until your score is a zero. Use the same procedure as I have suggested for phobias in chapter eight. Just keep on going until you have collapsed them all.

Sometimes when you are using EFT, you may be working with an issue of, say, guilt, and realise that the feeling is now more accurately described as shame; or anger, and realise that the feeling is now more one of hurt. If this happens, and it feels right, change your reminder phrase to suit these new feelings.

It is fine to do this halfway through the sequence; it will have no ill effect on the process. However, if another, unconnected, issue comes into your mind (as opposed to another aspect of the same issue) it is probably best to start on this new issue after you have collapsed the current one. Just jot it down and come back to it later.

Be specific in your statements and persistent in your application of EFT and your results should improve.

Be Specific

I cannot stress enough the importance of an accurate, truthful set-up statement. Make sure the statement rings true to you. EFT will do what is asked of it, so you must be very clear about what you are asking for.

Use your own language. Your subconscious speaks the same language as you do. If you are working on PMS, for example, and the phrase you use in your head to describe the pain is 'crippling gut's ache', use this for your set-up statement, not 'this pain in my tummy'.

Similarly, if you have festering negative feelings towards a work colleague who is a 'pain in the neck' or a 'wind-up merchant', use these expressions in your set-up statement. To experience the best outcome, you must direct EFT exactly where you want it to go.

Toxins

If your body contains toxins, which could include things like wheat, dairy produce, caffeine, nicotine, alcohol etc, this could hinder the healing processes of EFT.

If you are having no success with EFT, it is worth while taking a good look at your diet, maybe even cutting out suspect foods one by one and seeing if this makes any difference. A kinesiologist could help you in this respect and test you for possible food allergies.

Your surroundings could also contain pollutants which prevent healing from taking place, but this is rare. I have only had one experience when toxins were present in the atmosphere and prevented progress being made, and that was when I was working with a lady in her own home.

We were tapping away at her issue and getting absolutely no movement. This was causing her some distress, as she had been recommended to try EFT by a friend who had experienced healing using EFT, and when we started the session she was full of hope. Over a period of six years, she had tried 'every therapy going', and after her friend's success with EFT she was feeling that this may at last be the lifeline she had been searching for.

As the session progressed with no resolution of her issue, she was losing this hope and getting visibly distressed about it. I questioned her about her diet but she ate very healthily, avoided foods that she had learned she was allergic to, didn't drink tea, coffee or alcohol and was a non-smoker.

I told her that although I had no personal experience of it, during my studies of EFT I had learned that, although rare, sometimes the environment in which EFT is being performed could affect the healing process. I suggested that we try going into the garden.

It was a beautiful day and she was lucky enough to have a large garden with a pond, so we went outside to the end of her garden, sat down beside it and started again. Immediately we began to get results. By the end of our session, she had resolution of a profound issue that had weighed her down for seven years.

So, if you are getting nowhere, try moving to another room or going outside into the fresh air and starting again.

Exercises

There are a couple of exercises that you could try which may help clear any remaining obstacles to healing. If you have lowered your score to, say 1 or 2, and it stubbornly refuses to go any lower even though you are sure you have covered all the aspects that surround your issue, try this exercise:

Floor To Ceiling Eye Roll Exercise

Keep your head perfectly still and look down as far as you possibly can. Repeating your reminder phrase and tapping the gamut point, take six seconds to slowly raise your eyes to look up as high you possibly can. This exercise can often collapse the remaining intensity to zero and only takes a few seconds to perform.

Collarbone Breathing Exercise

If you have been persistent in your application of EFT, have exhausted all the possible impediments to the process that you can think of, and still have not succeeded in reducing your score to zero, try starting each round of EFT with the Collarbone Breathing Exercise which is carried out as follows.

With your arms held away from your body, place the pads of the first and middle fingers of your right hand onto your right collarbone point and tap the gamut point continuously with two fingers of your left hand. Still tapping, do the following breathing exercise.

1. Breathe in halfway and hold your breath for seven taps
2. Breathe all the way in and hold your breath for seven taps
3. Breathe halfway out and hold your breath for seven taps
4. Breathe all the way out and hold for seven taps
5. Breathe normally for seven taps

Repeat this with the fingers of your right hand placed on your left collarbone point.

Now bend the two fingers of your right hand and place them on your right collarbone point with the second knuckles making contact. Tap the gamut point continuously and perform the breathing exercise again.

Repeat this with the right knuckles placed on the left collarbone point.

Now, simply repeat the whole exercise again, using the fingers and knuckles of your left hand on your collar bone point and tapping the gamut point with your right hand. Remember to keep your arms away from your body at all times.

Delayed Reaction

With some people, there can be a delay before the effects of EFT 'kick in'. If you feel you have not had as much success as you would wish for, revisit your problems in a few days time and compare your present SUDS score with your score before you applied EFT. You are likely to find it has lowered.

Keep at it. Be persistent in your efforts and specific in your set up phrases and don't give it up as a bad job. If you use EFT three or four times a day, more if you can manage it, even the seemingly impossible cases should, over a short period of time, lose their emotional impact.

This chapter gives you a few suggestions to help clear any remaining blockages that may be present. However, the best advice I can give you is to keep at it. Although we regularly and frequently experience 'One Minute Wonders' with EFT, this is not always the case and I cannot stress enough the importance of being persistent.

Chapter Seven

Physical Pain

*"Pain (any pain--emotional, physical, mental) has a
message.......once we get the pain's message, and
follow its advice, the pain goes away"*
Peter McWilliams, Life 101

EFT is truly a universal healing aid. As well as
emotional issues, it is very adept at removing pain.
There is only one reason we feel pain, and that is
because something is wrong Some pain has an
obvious root, such as a physical injury, a stiff neck
when you have been hunched over books, or the
pain many women experience during stages of
their menstrual cycle. Other pain can have a less
obvious, emotional root.

When your pain is caused by a physical injury,
think of EFT as a paracetamol and be prepared for
the pain to return after a while. Remember, the
reason the pain is there is to warn you to take care.
The pain *will* go by applying EFT to it, but please be
careful and allow your body to heal before you do
anything too strenuous.

You need to formulate a truthful statement which best describes your pain. Be specific. Instead of choosing "this headache", you might use:

"Even though I have this blinding headache, I deeply and completely accept myself"

"Even though I have this dull ache behind my eyes, I deeply and completely accept myself"

"Even though I feel this tension in my temples, I deeply and completely accept myself"

"Even though my head is all fuzzy, I deeply and completely accept myself"

You will also need a 'reminder phrase' for the tapping procedure, and once again, this is taken from your original statement. In the examples we have used the reminder phrase would be:

'This blinding headache'.

'This dull ache behind my eyes'.

'This tension in my temples'.

'My fuzzy head'.

Now give your pain a score and start to apply your first round of EFT. Remember to stay focused on your pain while you are doing this. With EFT, focusing on the issue you are working with is very important.

When you have finished your first round of EFT, measure the result. Focus on your pain and once more give it a score. Hopefully you will have moved down 2 or three points, maybe more. This must be reflected in the next round of EFT.

Just as with emotional issues, you must address the problem as it is now, not as it was when you started. Your statement should now be:

"Even though I *still* have *some* of this blinding head- ache, I deeply and completely accept myself".

"Even though I *still* have *some* of this dull ache behind my eyes, I deeply and completely accept myself".

"Even though I *still* have *some* of this tension in my temples, I deeply and completely accept myself".

"Even though I *still* have *some* fuzziness in my head, I deeply and completely accept myself"

With the reminder phrases:

'This *remaining* headache'

'This *remaining* ache behind my eyes'

'This *remaining* tension in my temples'

'This *remaining* fuzziness in my head'

Use these statements and reminder phrases for the second and any subsequent rounds that are necessary.

Test your score after each complete application of EFT and keep going until it reaches zero. The test for EFT and physical pain is... "Does it hurt anymore?"

Chasing The Pain

Sometimes, you will find that the site of the pain moves, maybe several times. In these circumstances, you just keep applying EFT to the new site of the pain until you have chased it away.

When the site of the pain moves, it is usually a clue that it has an emotional root. Physical pain often has an emotional root. When applying EFT to a physical pain, if a memory or a realisation of an emotional issue pops into your head, take note.

Apply EFT to this and any surrounding thoughts or aspects that you can think of. Keep at it until your SUDS score is a zero and you are sure there are no more aspects left. This is a wonderful chance for you to clear that issue away.

Chapter Eight

Fears and Phobias

"They can conquer who believe they can"
Virgil (70 BC - 19 BC)

Most phobias originate from a personal experience, sometimes long forgotten (The core issue). Fears and phobias will usually have many, many aspects to them. For EFT to do its job properly, each aspect must be hunted down and tapped away.

A phobia is defined in the Collins English Dictionary as 'an abnormal, intense and irrational fear of a given situation, organism or object. *From the Greek phobus, fear'*.

Note the use of the word 'abnormal'. When standing close to a cliff edge, a 'normal' reaction is to be aware it is a danger and to take care not to do anything that might end up with you in a pile at the foot of it.

An 'abnormal' reaction is to assume that if you go anywhere near it, certain death awaits you!

The most common phobias are heights, spiders and flying. Let's look at flying.

This fear has numerous aspects. If you took this fear and applied EFT using the statement "Even though I have this fear of flying, I deeply and completely accept myself", the chances are that you would lower your SUDS score by 1 or 2. But ... if you started at a 10 this means you are still experiencing discomfort to the tune of 8 or 9. This is a big number when we are aiming for zero.

You may even lower your score to a 2 or 3, with the thought of flying hardly impacting at all on an emotional level, and think you are 'cured'. But, when you confidently arrive at the airport, expecting it to be plain sailing 'because I've tapped for it', all those awful sensations will come rushing back with a vengeance.

You will say to yourself something along the lines of "I knew EFT was too good to be true" and file away the whole experience in that drawer marked 'The A - Z of Failures'. But, it's not that EFT hasn't done its job; it's just that you've only addressed one aspect of the fear.

Let me explain. There are many aspects related to the fear of flying and each of these aspects might have different SUDS scores.

For example, you might not experience the same discomfort when booking the flight (let's say a 2 or 3) as you do when the 'plane takes off (which is probably a 10!) But, to clear the phobia completely, we must neutralise every frisson of fear that feeds it.

The list of aspects drawn up below and on the following page has been taken from my own case history files.

- Booking the flight
- Tickets arriving in the post
- Making 'holiday lists'
- Packing
- Setting off for the airport
- Seeing the 'planes queuing when approaching the airport.
- Arriving at the airport
- Checking in
- Waiting for the flight to be called
- Walking to the 'plane
- Boarding the 'plane
- Fear of losing control & running off the 'plane
- Pushing people aside
- Feeling claustrophobic

- Not liking so many people so close
- The door closing and shutting you in
- What if the door isn't closed properly?
- Will it be ripped off mid-flight and suck me to my death?
- Panic attacks
- The noise of the engines starting
- What if the engineer forgot about a vital nut & bolt?
- The taxiing to the runway
- Speeding along the runway
- The take-off
- The climb
- The heart-stopping moment when you think it is going to plummet to the ground
- Turbulence
- Fear of a hi-jack
- Fear of crashing
- Fear of dying
- When the 'plane banks
- Feeling air-sick
- The descent and landing

As you can see, it is a pretty comprehensive list. Thirty-three aspects in all. In fact it is so long, you would be forgiven for thinking that I specialised in this area and have clients beating a path to my door with their flying phobias!

Amazingly, thus far I have only treated two clients with this phobia, both of them successfully. Some of these aspects were common to both clients, but not all. So as you can see, some phobias can have countless aspects. What a mammoth task this is!

Mammoth it may be, monumental even, but EFT likes nothing more than getting stuck into a seemingly insurmountable problem...and clearing it, aspect by aspect, until nothing but the memory remains.

No shakes, no anxiety, no sleepless nights of worry. Nothing but the memory, which, once its emotional sting has been removed, has as much impact upon you as the memory of a trip to the butcher to buy some sausages!

When you are working with an issue which has many aspects, don't expect too much of yourself. Don't give up if you run out of the time you have allowed yourself for the session. Allow yourself some more time. You owe it to both EFT and to yourself.

Think how many aspects there were in the example of the flying phobias. Although a round of EFT takes only minutes to perform, if you are working on a lot of aspects and each one takes maybe two or three rounds those minutes will add up. It might take a few sessions to clear them all. Take the time you need. You deserve it. Be persistent and you will succeed!

So, when you feel confident enough to work on your phobia, take a sheet of paper and lay it out as shown below. This is to monitor your progress through the healing process.

Write your fear or phobia here					
Aspects	SUDS score at start	SUDS score after 1st round	SUDS score after 2nd round	SUDS score after 3rd round	SUDS score after 4th round

Across the top of the page in big, bold letters, write the name of the fear or phobia you are working on. In the first column, write a list of any aspects that you imagine might be connected with it, one on each line.

This part may cause you a small amount of discomfort, but to minimise this, don't try to recall each one in detail, just write it down as it pops into your head, give it a score and move quickly on to the next. If you find it difficult to judge what the score might be, just take a guess. You will know whether the score is lowering, wherever it started.

Remember, we are looking for a true statement of the way you are feeling about your fear now, in the present moment, not a score of the way you felt the last time your phobia manifested itself. With EFT, you work on the way you feel now, not the way you felt then. When you have finished your list, you are ready to start.

Now, apply EFT to the first aspect on the list, exactly as you did before. Go right through the complete sequence, and then write down your new score in the column entitled 'suds after 1st round'. If it is not zero, keep applying EFT to this aspect and assessing your score until you have lowered it to zero.

Then apply EFT to the second aspect, then the third and so on until you get to the bottom of the list and successfully neutralise all the aspects of your issue. During this process, you might find other aspects are brought to mind which you hadn't thought about when you were making your list.

Add these to your list if and when they arise, and apply EFT to them, too, either immediately, by adjusting your reminder phrase and focus; when you have finished the aspect you are working on; or when you reach them on the list - whichever feels right for you. Very often, applying EFT to a phobia will bring the core issue to the surface, with the opportunity to effect profound healing.

When you feel confident that you have neutralised all your aspects, imagine yourself coming face to face with your fear. If there are aspects you haven't covered, you will still feel some discomfort. Identify these lingering aspects and work through them as before. Be persistent until you have chased them all away.

When you can imagine yourself in a previously phobic situation without any negative emotional impact, the healing process is complete. You will find that when you meet circumstances that previously caused you great problems, they will have no adverse effects on you at all.

Chapter Nine

Stress

"If you are distressed by anything external,
the pain is not due to the thing itself, but your estimate
of it, and this you have the power to revoke at any moment."
Marcus Aurelius, AD121-180

One of the things I have learned in my practice of complementary therapy is that our body always tells us when something is wrong. It doesn't always 'use its head' and speak to us in words or thoughts, but it has ways and means of telling us that all is not well and it needs a little attention.

We are not usually very good at tuning into our body's language and often the signals it is sending to us are ignored. Our bodies do not like being ignored.

Pain is one of the body's methods of telling us that something is wrong and we need to get it sorted. We have ways of removing the pain, with EFT or with various medications. But unless we deal with the root cause, the pain will return, quite often with a vengeance.

Take the body's need for water. Our brains and bodies are mostly made up of water, 65% and 90% respectively. Without water we cannot function. When we feel thirsty, it is our body telling us that we need more liquid input. We take a drink of water and this assuages our thirst. Problem solved.

But what would happen if we ignored the thirst?

If we don't take that drink, our body is likely to step up a level and give us a headache. Even then, if we take a drink of water the headache will go away. Problem solved.

If we were to take a pill instead, the headache will go away but the problem is **not** solved. The headache will come back again. The root cause remains. We need a drink, and until we take one our body is going to carry on giving us stronger and stronger signals until eventually we would collapse.

All because we ignored the signals our body was sending us, telling us it needed water. If we had taken a drink as soon as we felt thirsty, there would be no problem.

So it is with stress. Our body tells us when it is stressed, if we listen to it. No-one can avoid stress. Stress is a part of life. It can be the driving force that fills us with excited tension at the joy of achievement or the anticipation of a special event. The body is flooded with adrenalin and we 'go with the flow'. We feel good. We are on a 'high'. We are firing on all cylinders. It keeps us alert and enthusiastic and enables creative energies to flow. This is positive stress.

Then there is 'normal' stress, which occurs as a reaction to an abnormal event. In situations that are perceived as dangerous, the body is again flooded with adrenalin, prepared for the 'flight or fight' choice to be made.

Time may go into slow motion. Our logical, decision-making processes shut down, our reptilian brain takes over and our primitive survival instincts are uppermost. Because our logical brain isn't on duty to tell us otherwise, we are capable at these times of feats of great strength, even heroism, that we would never think ourselves capable of in our everyday lives.

Mothers have even lifted cars off their children at times like these! We have the capability of doing what is necessary at the moment of danger. Plenty of time to collapse later when the danger is past and the body can get back to normal again.

These types of stress are healthy functions of our bodies' innate desire to keep us safe and well. After the stress has passed, the para-sympathetic functions of the body come into play and adjust all the levels of chemicals in our body back into balance again. The problems arise when we experience continuous high levels of stress. There is no chance for the para-sympathetic systems to function effectively and so we remain in a permanent state of stress. This is negative stress and we really don't want it. Our bodies weren't designed to function at this level and this is when stress becomes distress.

Negative stress can be emotional, physical, mental or a mixture of these. To take care of ourselves, we need to view all these parts as a whole. In a perfect world, we would be aware of subtle changes in our body, acknowledge the cause and deal with it. Treated this way, any imbalances would be short lived.

But we don't live in a perfect world. There is so much going on in our lives that we don't listen to our bodies. We sink to deeper depths of distress as our bodies send out stronger and stronger signals in the hope that we will do something about it.

One of the first signs that there is something wrong is often tiredness and/or headaches. You will be doing yourself an enormous favour if, as well as dealing with these symptoms, you take a good look at what the possible cause could be. It may be glaringly obvious, as in the case of death or divorce, but if the cause is not clear to you, turn detective. Search for the cause and address it, before it becomes a more serious matter.

It could be work related, family problems, guilt, something as simple as too many late nights, even a hangover! For your own well-being, find the cause and deal with it.

The Spiral Of Stress

Tiredness and headaches are early warning signals. Ignored, they can develop into insomnia, then irritability, caused by lack of sleep. Your body is telling you to stop. It is stressed. It needs to repair itself, but it can't do it without your help ... and you are not listening.

So it starts to shout. You begin to feel anxious. You start to suffer from 'unexplained' aches and pains, your muscles are tired and aching and you feel apathetic. You can't sleep, and when you eventually do, you suffer nightmares.

Your immune system weakens and you start to get cold sores and spots. You feel guilty because you think you should be able to 'snap out of it'. The fact that you can't makes you feel depressed. You feel helpless, trapped, out of control.

If there is no intervention, the stress continues on its downward spiral. At this level of stress, the symptoms become more severe. Because your immune system has been weakened, you are an easy target for any virus or bacteria that is doing the rounds. Even an invasion of the common cold virus can render you seriously ill. Phobias and complexes can begin to take root. The guilt becomes more unbearable.

The body is breaking down. It is shouting for help at the top of its voice, but you don't understand the language.

High blood pressure, heart problems, strokes, irritable bowel syndrome, ulcers, arthritis, all these are thought to have their roots in stress. It is also believed that stress is the cause of some cancers. Certainly all of these conditions are made worse by the presence of stress.

Learn your body's language. Listen to what it is saying to you and act on the information received. Your body is your best friend. Your survival is important to it, and its survival is important for you. Mind, body, spirit. All need each other to survive and function as a complete human being.

If you take the time to get to know your body, and how it 'feels' in different situations, you are in a better position to notice when something feels 'not quite right' and do something about it, thus preventing the body from having to shout at you.

With EFT you can tap away tensions as they arise. If you don't know why you are tense/anxious try tapping along the lines of:

"Even though I don't know why I'm tense (or anxious, or worried etc.) I deeply and completely accept myself"

"Even though I don't feel quite right, I deeply and completely accept myself"

I know it sounds silly, but this approach often calls the issue to the mind, which can then be scored on the SUDS scale as before, and tapped away!

Negative Thinking

Negative thinking does us no good at all. It leads eventually to dis-ease. All of us do it at some time or another. It is **guaranteed** to make us feel bad but we still do it. It is de-motivating and de-moralising.

It steals our enthusiasm, raises our anxiety levels, saps our energy and interferes with concentration. It lowers self-esteem and changes our perspective on the world. And now it is being scientifically proved that it affects our health.

Since the 1980s, with the founding of the Psychoneuroimmunology Research Society (PNIRS), scientists and doctors involved with neuroscience, immunology, integrative physiology, behavioural biology, psychiatry, psychology and clinical medicine (in layman's language, experts from all different aspects of human medicine and behaviour) have been researching and carrying out basic, experimental and clinical studies; discovering and sharing how behavioural, neural, endocrine and immune systems interact, in both humans and animals.

Their discoveries show that all our various bodily systems are not separate entities, but a very complicated network of systems which work together as a whole; interacting with each other to keep our bodies at an optimum level of health and vitality. Their research has shown that our different states of mind have a measurable physiological effect on our bodies.

Negative thinking **measurably** suppresses our immune system and lays us open to disease. Negative thoughts, and the afterthoughts we talked about earlier in chapter six, play a major role 'behind the scenes' in the shaping of our health, lives and relationships.

Without us considering them or even realising what is going on, these thoughts become part of the acquired knowledge of our unconscious minds. It is this acquired, uncensored knowledge which colours any sort of decision we may have to make.

Positive thoughts also have a measurable, effect on the body's performance. Positive, happy thoughts, and laughter, stimulate the body into manufacturing serotonin and endorphins, which give us that 'feel good' background to our lives. Positive thoughts can help alleviate stress and EFT can help in this process.

Several rounds of EFT a day, using the set-up statement: "Even though I have negative thoughts I choose to think positively" or "When I have a negative thought I choose to stop and look for the positive" can bring about remarkable results.

It is so easy to get carried away by negative thoughts but applying a round of EFT, morning and evening, using these two statements and the reminder phrases "I choose to look for the positive" and " I choose to think positively" will help you recognise these thoughts and think twice.

There will always be a positive side if you look hard enough, there cannot be a negative without a positive. Each is one side of a whole.   Thoughts are our own creation. These are **your** thoughts, in **your** head, and **you** can consciously decide their direction.

Once you start to gain confidence in your use of EFT and notice the subtle changes which are taking place in your perspective, as well as the more obvious benefits, you'll never look back.

Chapter Ten

Trauma

*"It is slavery to live in the mind unless it
has become part of the body".*
Kahlil Gibran (1883 - 1931)

People who suffer a trauma react in different ways. For some it is just something terrible that happened to them, they manage to deal with it and it doesn't impact on their daily lives. For some, it can lead to a phobia which is rooted in the trauma, often unconsciously.

For an unfortunate few, flashbacks of the traumatic event can happen at any time, with all the accompanying emotions and sensations of that moment. This extreme reaction is known as Post-Traumatic Stress Disorder (PTSD). EFT can literally be a life saver for sufferers of this syndrome.

If you are working with a traumatic event which has many aspects, such as a car crash, or a rape, a useful way of finding and collapsing the many different aspects that will be present is to use the 'movie technique'.

It is a method that is used in many conventional 'talk' therapies, as well as in complementary and alternative therapies. It distances you from the event and allows you to view your part in the trauma as something that is happening to someone else, not to yourself. This is known as 'dissociation'

Most traumatic events are viewed as a 'flash' memory. By running a movie, frame by frame, scene by scene, it enables you to break down the event into the different aspects that will be present. The movie technique, used along with EFT, allows painless, profound healing to ensue.

When you are ready to begin, think of a title for your movie. If you begin to experience discomfort, do a round of EFT with the set-up statement of

"Even though I feel anxious about working on (your movie title) I deeply and completely accept myself"

until the feeling passes, then you are ready to begin.

In my opinion, combining the movie technique with EFT has the edge over other talk therapies which use this technique.

Used with EFT, you have the ability to stop and tap at the first sign of discomfort. Painless healing is our aim here. There is no need to 'face the fear and feel the pain' with EFT.

You have tried EFT on something and it works for you. I am confident about this. You wouldn't be about to try it on your trauma if you had not had good, positive experiences with EFT. Remember the discovery statement?

"The cause of all negative emotions is a disruption of the boy's energy system"

Don't try to be brave. Any disruption is unnecessary with EFT.

The first thing you must do when you are working on a trauma with the movie technique is establish a safe place to return to. This is very important. You do this by setting the first scene of your movie at a time just prior to the event; before you were aware of what was going to happen, where you felt safe; and then consciously note how your body feels. Become familiar with these safe feelings.

Then you set the last scene at a point in time after the event, when you again felt safe, and once again consciously experience the feelings of safeness. Become familiar with the way your body feels when you are in these safe settings.

This now places your trauma into a definite time frame, in between these two safe places. Imagine you are running your movie on a screen in front of you. You are the projectionist and if you feel any discomfort at any point, stop the film and apply EFT, or rewind/fast forward to either of your safe places and stay there while you tap your discomfort away.

Remember: stop your movie and apply EFT at the **first** *sign* of discomfort. If a powerful emotion rushes up and catches you unawares, go straight to the first or last scene, where you know you are safe. Stay there, applying EFT, until there is nothing left of it and you feel you can happily move forward. Please don't try to be brave; gritted teeth and willpower are unnecessary with EFT!

When you have established your safe place it is time to start the movie. Start at scene one, in your safe place, and move forward until you start to experience discomfort. Score your discomfort and apply EFT to this aspect of your traumatic memory until it is zero, and then start the film again.

When you get to the part which caused you the discomfort, check that it is gone. If you still experience any discomfort, even just a score of 1, don't go any further. Go back to the start and tap away the residual discomfort. This is a healing process not a battle; and you get no brownie points for bravery.

Continue in this way until you can run the whole film without any discomfort. Then play the film in slow motion, frame by frame, to check if there was anything you missed. If this is the case, do as before: return to scene one, tap away your discomfort, then move the film forward in slow motion again.

When you can successfully play the whole movie with no emotional discomfort, it is time to test the result more fully. Play the movie again; but this time, instead of being the projectionist watching the movie, put yourself into the movie and imagine it happening to you, in person, instead of you in the film.

In the same way as before, start in your safe place and move forward, scene by scene, checking that there is no aspect left in the movie that causes you any discomfort. Should you feel any at all, stop and tap it away.

When you have successfully collapsed all your negative emotions you should never be troubled by that particular trauma ever again.

If the original trauma was ongoing, such as active service in war, or systematic abuse, there may be many traumatic memories involved, even hundreds, each with its own aspects. This is not a problem for EFT.

If you have many traumatic memories with a similar root and start working through them, one by one, a wonderful thing happens.

Once you start to address these memories with EFT, a 'generalization effect' usually takes place. When you have worked with 10 or so of them, and go looking for the next one to deal with, you will probably find that the generalization effect has neutralised some of the remaining memories as well!

What a wonderful thing this EFT is!

Chapter Eleven

EFT and Children

*"Don't limit a child to your own learning,
for he was born in another time"*
Rabbinical Saying

Children are wonderfully receptive to EFT. They have no reason to believe that tapping, singing, and rolling your eyes in your head is a 'wrong' way of doing things. They know it's a different way, but that's usually OK by them. Their belief systems are not yet carved in granite!

When working with children, the uses of EFT are as numerous as there are children! It is an amazing tool.

EFT can rid a child of fear and guilt and shame and grief. EFT can be used help them sleep and free them from nightmares. EFT can be used to build their confidence and self-esteem. EFT can be used to assist them in their social lives.

EFT can be used to stop them biting their nails. EFT can be used to improve their concentration and their studying. Whenever a child is less than 100% happy and balanced, EFT can help.

I have successfully treated these issues in children with EFT:

- Anger
- Grief
- Guilt
- Shame
- Nightmares
- Unfairness - (children have a highly refined sense of what is and isn't fair!)
- Fear - of needles, dragons and death, to name but a few.
- Not being good enough
- Great sadness
- Excitability
- Pain

The process is the same. You identify the problem, give it a score and off you go. With a child, it is often easier and no less effective to use the karate chop point instead of the sore spot. If it's not the child or Mum who is applying the technique, but a friend or therapist, this is probably the best choice.

The approach used for a child is different from that used for an adult, and should be tailored to their age and personal needs. Most children, even the very young, enjoy the sensations they experience when EFT is applied to them. They are quick to pick up the technique but are usually very happy to receive it from some-one else as well.

For the set up statement, instead of "I deeply and completely accept myself", which probably wouldn't mean a lot to a five year old child who has fallen out with their best friend, choose something positive, like

"I'm OK"
"Mummy/Daddy loves me"
"I'm a nice person"

Learn to trust your instincts to help with the phrase that is right for your child in the given circumstances, and to make sure the child 'feels' right when they say it.

If there has been a death or divorce in the family, it is well known that children will often take on the blame, and then they carry guilt around with them. If the death was sudden, fear is another emotion commonly felt by children. They can be afraid that they, or the other people around them, are going to die, too.

If they are suffering emotional pain (my words not theirs), it is a good idea for them to place their hand over the affected area, as children often cannot define a feeling in words but usually know where they are carrying the pain (the hurt). This is often around the heart and solar plexus area.

So, for example, if a much-loved Grandad has died, you could ask them to show you where it hurts and use something along the lines of the following:

"Even though this really hurts I'm strong"

"Even though I'm really unhappy I know Grandad doesn't want me to be sad"

"Even though I'll never see Grandad again, I'll always remember him"

"Even though Grandad has died, it doesn't mean everyone else will"

Be inventive. Use a statement that rings with the truth as the child sees it, and keep going until they are calm and relaxed. If they are crying, say the words for them.

You can use EFT to calm babies and young children and soothe them to sleep. You can use EFT to stop the pain when a child falls over. You can use EFT to free them of their fears. You can even use EFT to stop them fighting each other!

This is something we can all do for our children, a practise which takes no time at all to learn and yet is so full of promise.

Children seem to be more aware of the shifts and changes which take place in their energy systems during EFT and they thoroughly enjoy the experience, especially afterwards when they realise that their problem is not there anymore. I have seen an eight year old girl tapping her 4 year old cousin because he was very upset and angry with his Mummy because he couldn't have a dog! She was doing it because "it always makes *me* feel better!"

Once they have experienced the cessation of a problem through EFT it easily integrates and becomes part of their belief system, and why not? What better tool could we give our children to take into their future?

EFT and Teenagers

For teenagers EFT is a wonderful tool, too. These days there is so much pressure on teenagers to succeed at everything. At a time in their lives when they have no control over the feelings produced by the hormones that are raging around preparing their bodies for maturity, they have to study, take exams and make huge life decisions.

While all this is going on, their perspective on the opposite sex is also changing, and we all know what that does to one's emotional balance! Teenagers fall in and out of love at the drop of a hat, and if all their relationships were synchronized it would all work out very well.

However, this is the real world and most teenagers will, at some time or another, be 'dumped'. Most will cry themselves to sleep for a time and then cast their eyes about for another.

But there are those who find it hard to accept that someone they had planned to love forever is now seeing someone else. EFT can take away that pain and the awful feelings of rejection, and help them feel loveable again.

Life is full of highs and lows for most teen-agers, and EFT can fill in some of the valleys so that the lows don't get too low, and the highs are more accessible. It can take away emotional pain from your child and keep their heads clear of negative thoughts; thoughts that, as we discover working with EFT, can so easily limit life's horizons. I have treated teenagers for

- Anger
- Guilt
- Being bullied
- Headaches
- Exam nerves
- Rejection
- Unfairness (again, as in younger children, that sense of justice!)
- Joint pain
- Love pain
- Feelings of unworthiness and low self esteem

As with younger children, the set up phrase can be adapted to suit the occasion, although older teenagers seem quite comfortable with "deeply and completely accept myself"

Once they have experienced it, teenagers tend to think EFT is 'cool'.

As with younger children, they kind of like the weirdness of EFT; and the fact that it also 'does the job' is a great plus! But, unlike younger children, who know that mum knows best, teenagers are more inclined to the belief that parents know nothing about anything, and can be reluctant to believe that they are, in fact, any use at all!

When they are in the middle of an emotional crisis that you couldn't *possibly* understand, telling them that they will feel better if you tap them might not meet with a favourable response!

A good way to raise their awareness of the potential of EFT as a universal healing tool is to introduce EFT to them as a remedy for a physical problem, i.e. headache, period cramps, stiff neck etc. Once they have experienced the dissipation of a physical pain, they are usually totally hooked and want to know all about it.

That gives you a great opening to discuss how EFT was actually designed to ease emotional suffering, and that it can be self-administered, which means it can be used for their emotional issues without having to tell anyone (especially their parents!!) their innermost secrets if they don't want to. This is a great plus for most teenagers.

Author's note: I would like to add that I am discussing 'normal' teenagers and life's 'normal' issues here. If you feel that your teenager's problems are more than either you or they can cope with, please seek professional help.

Case Histories

"As human beings, our greatness lies not so much in being able to remake the world as in being able to remake ourselves".
Mahatma Gandhi (1869 - 1948)

I have devoted a whole chapter of this book to case histories. We all love the case histories, don't we? I want to show you the diverse problems which can be helped by EFT. EFT truly is a universal healing aid. What else do you know which would give you freedom from phobias **and** get rid of your migraine **and** relieve your PMT symptoms?

You may relate to one of these cases, you may not. That doesn't matter. This is not a definitive list of what EFT can help with, and if your particular issue isn't included, that doesn't mean EFT won't help, it just means there aren't enough pages in this book...ten books even...to give an example of all the varied and different issues which have been resolved with EFT. All the names used are fictitious.

I have included 'one minute wonder' case histories, because they do happen with such regularity. Do not be pessimistic if this is not so in your case. Be persistent in your use of EFT and specific with your set up statements and you *will* get results. And believe me, a result is worth the time it takes you, however long that may be!

ANNE
Golfer's Elbow

Along with other issues, Anne had a problem with her elbow. It had been diagnosed as 'golfer's elbow', which is when the tendon on the inside of the elbow becomes torn and inflamed and painfully tender, as opposed to 'tennis elbow' which is the same problem on the outside of the elbow.

Any kind of lifting or reaching aggravated the condition and made it more painful. She was taking anti-inflammatory tablets and pain-killers every four hours; nevertheless her pain was 8 on a SUDS when we started. We applied three rounds of the complete EFT sequence, using the set-up statements:

"Even though I have this pain in my elbow I deeply and completely accept myself"

SUDS 4

"Even though I still have some of this pain I deeply and completely accept myself"

SUDS 1½

"I want to be completely free of this pain"

SUDS zero

She remained pain-free for four days, at which point she successfully addressed the pain herself with EFT. Thus far the problem has not returned but, in Anne's words, "If it does, I now know that I can get rid of it fast".

BRYONY
Sore Eye

Bryony is a bright eight year old. She visited with her mum, who, during the visit mentioned that Bryony was having a problem with her eye. With mum's agreement I approached Bryony and asked her what the problem was. She said she had a sore eye.

At the top of her cheekbone, under her left eye, there was an area which itched. She tried not to scratch it because that made it hurt more. I described EFT as a funny, silly little thing which might help make it better and showed her the places I would be tapping on. She was eager to give it a try.

I asked her how much it hurt and she said it was very sore rather than painful and scored it at 7. I asked her to repeat the set-up statement after me, while I tapped the karate point. The set-up statement I used was:

"Even though my eye is very sore, I'm OK."

We did the first round of tapping and 'the funny bit in the middle' which made her smile. On the second round, when I lifted her arm to tap underneath it she started to laugh. I asked her if she was ticklish. "No" she said "I'm laughing because my eye isn't sore any more"

CLAIRE
Migraine Attacks

Claire had suffered for several years from severe migraine attacks which considerably disrupted her everyday life. There was no obvious trigger. She would be migraine free for a couple of months and then suffer a cluster of attacks over a period of weeks.

The first sign of an attack was a ringing in her ears and a feeling of 'not being quite right'. This was followed by nausea and sometimes vomiting, accompanied by an intense, gripping pain behind her eyes, and her eyes and nose would run, as if she had a cold. This could last from a few hours to several days.

We were together one day when she started to experience her 'early warning signs' and I suggested we try EFT. I asked her if she had any idea what had triggered the attack but she gave a negative response. We used the following set-up statements, without scoring, and did one complete sequence for each statement.

"Even though I'm afraid I'm about to have one of my migraines, I deeply and completely accept myself."

"Even though I don't feel quite right, I deeply and completely accept myself."

"Even though I have this ringing in my ears, I deeply and completely accept myself."

During these rounds she expressed how calm and relaxed she was feeling, and by the time we had finished, she said she was feeling more like herself, and that the ringing in her ears had almost gone. We did another round using

"Even though I still have some of this ringing in my ears, I deeply and completely accept myself."

At this point the ringing in her ears stopped. She did not suffer a migraine attack that day and the usual cluster of attacks did not materialise. Seven months on she has not had another migraine attack.

DAVID
Constricted Breathing

I was talking to David about the wonders of EFT one day. He found it difficult to believe that what I was telling him was possible. David has always had a problem breathing through his nose, so I asked him to take as deep a breath as he could, through his nose, and to give it a score from 1 to 10, with 1 being very difficult and 10 being an easy lungful. He decided to humour me.

He scored it at 4 and it had not been easy for him. I showed him the tapping points and asked him to find and rub his sore spot and say:

"Even though I have difficulty breathing in through my nose, I deeply and completely accept myself."

I mirrored the tapping points for him as he went through the first round of tapping, repeating the reminder phrase. I performed the 9 Point Gamut for him and we went through the second round of tapping in the same way as the first.

I then asked him to take breath and score it. To his total amazement, without even blowing his nose, sneezing or sniffing, his score had gone up to a 9!

EDWARD
Sciatica

Edward had sciatica. The pain extended from the centre of his left buttock and down through his left leg. He described the pain as tolerable in certain positions, crippling in others.

Getting out of bed was a lengthy job. Walking upstairs was OK but coming down again was excruciating. The act of sitting down was more painful than standing up again. His score when he experienced this pain was off the scale!   We did a round of EFT using as the set-up statement:

"Even though I have this crippling pain, I deeply and completely accept myself."

I asked him to stand up and see if his score had lessened. He stood up and gingerly started bending from the waist. He looked puzzled. This is a very common reaction with EFT. It is hard to believe that chronic or acute pain can just not **be** there anymore!

"I don't believe it!" he said. He sat down. He stood up. He *wanted* to find the pain. "I know what'll do it," he said "the stairs!" and he left the room and went up and down my stairs twice, once slowly and once at a fast pace. No pain. It was gone.

FELICITY
PMS

I was playing cards with a friend one day, when she started to experience the acute pain which always heralded the start of her period. Her normal routine was to take a pain-killer and go to bed with a hot water bottle.

She agreed to be tapped. We used the setup statement:

"Even though my period pain has started, I deeply and completely accept myself"

One round of EFT and the pain was gone. Instead of the painkillers and bed, she happily continued, pain free, with our game.

GEMMA
Continuous Back Pain

(Testimonial)

"I am a 47 year old woman with an active life-style. For the past 18 months I have had constant pain in my hips and lower back that intensified with any attempts to bend forward. This constant pain, coupled with the inability to move freely was causing me to experience feelings of depression.

"Jean and I decided to tap for pain in the area of my lower back and hips, and upon the third tap the pain had miraculously disappeared.*

"To my surprise, when I stood up and bent forwards I could almost touch my toes! I did this many times without experiencing any pain or discomfort; the relief and joy I felt was over-whelming.

"My newly found mobility lasted for three months. I remain in awe of this brilliantly simple process that had such an immediate effect on my body.

*Author's note: at this point tears welled up, a familiar sign of emotional clearance.

"For me, EFT is a gentle yet powerful cathartic procedure that had an instant and profound effect on both my body and emotional well-being.

Many, many thanks to you Jean, for sharing with me this remarkable treasure, EFT."

HARRIET
Fear of flying & Emotional Anguish

(Letter)

About two years ago you suggested to me that we 'had a go' at this wonderful new therapy you had found out about. I was going on a holiday which involved a flight and was very anxious about flying. We 'tapped' for this anxiety, going through many rounds, considering all the specific aspects of the journey I found difficult to cope with.

Well, it worked (you know I had been sceptical!) I was also able to 'tap' at various stages of the journey and I can say I almost enjoyed the flight - a first!

But the real thank you I want to say is for how you really did 'save' me earlier this year.

I came to you distraught; my husband of over twenty years had ended our marriage. This was following my son being diagnosed with cancer and during his intensive chemotherapy.

I collapsed emotionally. I could not function at any level. The raw emotions I was experiencing frightened and overwhelmed me.

You spent so much time supporting me I can't thank you enough. Suffice it to say, with you using your EFT skills I was able to come through that terrible time.

I was able to return to a very demanding job, support my children and even smile again. At the times when the sadness or hurt returned, I was able to use the strategies you had taught me and relax again or move on - whatever was needed.

Use this letter to help other people if they need evidence for EFT - it works, although I also believe that it has to be the right person being the 'conduit' and you are definitely that right person.*

Thank you.

Author's note: I have to differ with Harriet here.

Undoubtedly, an experienced therapist is going to be more skilful in their mastery of the technique but, as she says earlier in her letter, this is a technique which you can very easily and successfully use yourself without having to depend on a therapist. This is one of the great joys of EFT...the low level of 'therapist dependency'

IVAN
Panic attacks and Insomnia

Ivan had been 'sent' by his wife to see me. He had trouble sleeping and when he did go to sleep he suffered from nightmares, waking up in a cold sweat, sometimes screaming. His recurring nightmare was of someone chasing him with a gun, but when this person tried to shoot him, another man appeared in front of him and was shot instead of him.

He had also recently started suffering from panic attacks at work when he felt he wasn't performing to his usual high standards. He had no idea what might have started it all off, but said he had been under a lot of stress at work.

In his first session we worked on his insomnia. I am a great believer in the importance of sleep. If you get a decent night's sleep I believe it gives you the ability to think straighter. We used the following set up-statement:

"Even though I can't sleep I deeply and completely accept myself"

Ivan could not verbalise "I deeply and completely accept myself". He was obviously struggling to remain in control so we did a few rounds of:

"Even though I don't accept myself,
I forgive myself"

"Even though I can't accept myself, I am
open to the possibility that I may be able to"

"Even though I can't accept myself, Elizabeth
(*his wife*) does"

He appeared much calmer, so again I tried:

"Even though I can't sleep I deeply and
completely accept myself"

and he was able to say it. We went on to:

"Even though I'm afraid to sleep in case
I have my nightmare, I deeply and completely
accept myself"

I then suggested we addressed his nightmare
using the 'movie technique' and told him to let me
know if any thoughts popped into his head.

After a couple of rounds he started to get
visibly distressed. I asked him what was upsetting
him and he said he had just had a thought about a
serious train accident he had been involved in four
years ago.

There had been many fatalities and horrific
injuries but he had escaped totally unscathed. He
had received counselling after the event and had
been taught various coping strategies. He had also

been prescribed anti-depressants. He had relocated to the Westcountry as he had found it impossible to travel to work on the train anymore. I explained that coping strategies were just that; strategies to enable you to push the memory and the pain back down again. EFT was designed to take away that emotional pain, usually permanently, not bury it deeper and pretend it's not there.

I also explained that although EFT cannot erase the memory, we could probably collapse this event, again using the movie technique, to a position where the memory loses its emotional sting and is no longer a problem. As this memory had come up during the EFT process, it was more than likely it was related to his nightmares and other symptoms of stress, therefore *now* would be the perfect time to address it. He was not prepared to face this and went home.

Three days later he rang me. He had suffered a panic attack in the middle of a business meeting and that night had had his nightmare again. This had made him decide he would try anything to get out of this "living hell".

His nightmare suggested he might well be suffering from 'survivor guilt' which is relatively common after such an event as a fatal train crash.

At his next session, before we started on his 'movie' of the crash, we did some rounds of:

"Even though I survived and others died, it is not my fault and I deeply and completely accept myself"

"Even though I didn't die and others did, I deeply and completely accept myself"

"Even though I escaped without a scratch I choose to forgive myself"

"I forgive myself, even though I feel there should have been something I could have done"

"I **know** I could not have prevented it"

"I **know** I am so lucky to be alive"

"Even though I survived where others died I choose to deeply and completely accept myself"

We then addressed all the aspects of the train crash. Several times throughout this session, Ivan was overwhelmed by tears and could not speak. At these points I carried on tapping, just repeating 'this feeling', 'this bad feeling' for him at each tapping point, until he felt ready to speak again. At this stage words are often unnecessary as the feelings are being actively experienced; Ivan was 'feeling' the negative emotion in the 'here and now', which is when EFT is at its most powerful.

I am happy to report that I have not seen Ivan again after that session. We have spoken several times on the phone and he has a copy of the EFT procedure, which he and his wife now use regularly to deal with issues as and when they arise.

He is now sleeping well. His nightmares and panic attacks have stopped. From his sceptical start he has turned into an evangelical believer.

When he starts to feel his stress levels rise at work, he takes himself off for five minutes to tap them away. He has also used EFT on some of his work colleagues!

JULIE
Spider phobia

Julie came to me with a fear of spiders. Intellectually she knew there was nothing to fear from spiders, but that didn't stop a full-blown panic attack when she spotted one. I had a picture of a spider and when I asked her if she would be comfortable looking at it, I got a very emphatic "NO!", so I guessed her SUDS score at 10 and we started working on some aspects of her fear.

- Their hairy legs

- The way they scuttle

- The way they suddenly appear

- The way they run towards you

- The way their bodies hang between their legs

- Walking into a web with a spider in the middle of it

She expressed how calm the EFT was making her feel as we worked through these aspects and brought them all down to a zero.

Then I asked her to imagine what her SUDS would be if she looked at the picture of the spider. She thought probably only about a 4 or 5 now. We tapped on her fear of looking at the picture until she came down to a 1 and said she'd try looking.

She had a little shudder as I turned it over but was surprised how calm she felt looking at it. However, she wasn't convinced this would help in a real situation, face to face with a real spider.

So I asked her to imagine a scene in which this happened, but the moment she felt any distress, even slightly, she was to stop and not go any further until we lowered her score to a zero.

She then remembered an occasion that had happened when she was a child, she thinks about 7 or 8 years old. She had forgotten the incident until now. This is her tale. We used the 'Tearless Trauma' technique. The heavy print is where we stopped and tapped until she felt comfortable enough to continue.

"I was playing in the park on the climbing frame with my best friend and there was a **big spider sitting in the middle of a web** underneath the slide. Some boys were there and started **poking at the web**. The spider started **scurrying**

across the web. My friend and I told them to stop but they **laughed at us and called us 'sissies'.**

One of them scooped the spider into his hands and **pretended to throw it at us.** We jumped from the frame and started to run away. **They were calling 'Get them! Get them!'** The boy with the spider couldn't catch my friend, **but two of them caught me and called out to him 'We've got her!'**

They held me down on the ground while the other one came over. **He held his hand out and the spider dropped from his hand and stopped about 6 inches from my face.** I turned my head sideways, screwed up my eyes and closed my mouth. **I was frightened it would drop in my mouth. I couldn't call for help.**

He must have shaken his hand because **I felt it drop on my ear and scurry up the side of my face, over my forehead and into my hair.** (*At this point Julie became extremely distressed*). **I was afraid to open my mouth to shout and I couldn't get away.**

Then my friend came over with my brother and he pulled them off. **I started screaming and screaming and couldn't stop.** I was hysterical. I was shaking and shaking my head but **I could still feel the spider in my hair.** Then my brother took me home and my dad said not to be so silly, **it was only a spider. He didn't understand."**

Julie again became very upset at this stage and expressed surprise that she felt this distress so strongly, so we tapped for

"Even though Dad didn't understand how awful it was"

"Even though Dad didn't understand it wasn't **only** a spider"

On the second statement, before we had reached the end of the 9 Gamut procedure, she released a big sigh and said that the feeling had completely gone.

She said that really, it **was** only a spider. She reached forward, picked up the photograph, and with a smile on her face she started to stroke the spider's legs; a thing she said she would never have even contemplated doing before this EFT session.

When she left, I told her that the aspects we had worked on would probably never be an issue again when she confronted a real spider, but if she did start to feel anxious it would probably be some aspect we hadn't covered and she should tap herself for it.

About an hour later, I received a telephone call from her. She had felt so confident that when she got home she had gone into her garage where she knew there was a very big spider and confronted it. She said she had experienced none of her previous adverse reaction, but didn't think she wanted to stroke it, thank you very much!

This is an example of how EFT can get to the core issue in an amazingly short time. The root cause of her fear was the long forgotten incident in the playground, and her father's dismissal of how terrible she had felt. Seeing a spider triggered the memories of her emotions at that time. Once we had found the core issue and tapped away those original emotions, Julie was free of her phobia.

KARL
Grief and Anger

I had a lady come to see me with many issues, one of which was her concern for her son, Karl. Three years ago her 24 year old brother, Bill (who lived with them and shared a bedroom with Karl) went on holiday. Whilst away he died, suddenly and violently, and it had greatly affected Karl who was now eight years old.

From a bright, loving 5 year old who loved going to his new school, he changed. His work was suffering and he was having special needs tuition. His anger often over-spilled at moments of stress and so he was also seeing a behavioural therapist. I said I thought EFT would help him too (Mum and I had had a successful session) and I suggested she brought him along to see me.

I like to keep sessions for children as light-hearted and full of hope as I can. After gaining rapport with the child I said to him that his mummy had told me he felt very angry about his Uncle Bill and that I had this sort of clever, silly 'magic thing'*

*Author's note: I feel very comfortable using the word 'magic' with children who are of an age to believe in it. When their problems are huge, which sadly they often are, they can feel that nothing could ever make them better. Magic fits the bill beautifully, and EFT **is** the next best thing to magic!!)*

I did which might be able to 'chase away' his anger. Did he want to try it?   Yes, he would, because he didn't *like* being angry.

I asked him to show me how angry he was, held my arms out to measure as a fisherman would, about shoulder width apart moving them in and out, and said something like "This much? You show me" and he stretched his arms as wide as he could and said "This big".

I validated the extent of his anger by saying that that was an awful lot of anger for such a little boy to be carrying around with him and said how glad I was that his Mummy knew about 'this magic tapping stuff' and had brought him to see me.

I showed him, on myself, *where* the tapping points were and he copied my actions. I checked he was happy about them being tapped and asked him if he was ready to have a go. I formulated the statement myself and used

"Even though I'm REALLY angry that Uncle Bill is dead, I'm OK".

I used the karate spot and, as 'magic' had been mentioned, I did the tapping. I only used the tapping points on his eyebrow, under his eye, collarbone, under his arm and the karate point.

When we got to the 'funny bit in the middle' I chose the theme from Blue Peter as the tune, which made him smile and I responded with "You didn't know Blue Peter was such a clever song, did you?" I did the full 9 gamut. Children love this bit because it is so weird! It is definitely quirky and offers a bit of light relief in the middle.

Then another short round of tapping as before. "Right, let's see how much we've chased away so far" I said. He held his arms wide and then moved them together until his palms met. I joked "Are you clapping me or measuring?" (although I already knew the answer by his face).

He said, very seriously, "I can't measure for you, there isn't any left" and then a huge smile spread over his face. It was wonderful, and it happened in no time at all.

I asked if he needed anything else 'magicked' away. He said he was having trouble doing his work because his head was full of Uncle Bill. He thought this might be OK now he wasn't angry any more, but he'd like some more anyway, please, just in case; so we did a round on:

"Even though I couldn't concentrate on my work because I was thinking of Uncle Bill all the time, it's OK now I'm not angry anymore"

I chose the past tense because it 'felt' right.

Speaking to Mum a few days later, she said he had come out of school the following day and told her he had worked REALLY hard all day and not thought of Uncle Bill once.

On the way home in the car he was telling his friend about the lady "who knew magic and she tapped me and made me feel better"

LAURA
Negative Feelings and PMS

Laura's issue was one of negative feelings towards her husband. She thought the effects of two difficult births had probably 'messed her up down there' because she had felt no sexual desire for her husband since the children were born. She had never refused his sexual advances, because she loved him dearly, but she was beginning to resent them.

Being Catholic she took her marriage vows very seriously and, as she put it, "If this is for life, I need some help here"

We worked together on her problem. In the first session we used the set-up statements:

"Even though I don't feel any desire for John, I deeply and completely accept myself"

"Even though I feel resentful when John wants sex, I really love him"

"Even though having children 'messed me up down there" I deeply and completely accept myself"

After this last round Laura remembered her mother telling her, when she was a teenager, that the purpose of sex was procreation and that once children came along "...thank goodness there wasn't any need to have sex anymore". So we tapped on:

"Even though mum told me there was no need for sex once I have children,
that was her view, not mine"

"Even though sex has become a chore that I resent, I am confident this feeling will pass"

This last statement produced tears. Laura told me that she had always enjoyed sex with her husband before the children came along and was afraid that she would never enjoy it again. She was afraid that her husband would lose patience and find someone else. So we worked with

"Even though I am afraid I will never enjoy sex again I deeply and completely accept myself"

"Even though I am afraid John will leave me, I love and accept myself"

"I accept myself, even though I am scared John will find someone else"

This was the end of our session.

A week later Laura came back, a big smile on her face. She and her husband had left the children with his mother and gone away for the weekend, from Saturday morning until Sunday afternoon, and had had a wonderful time. She couldn't believe how different she felt.

She felt she didn't need to address the sexual issues any more, but wanted to know if EFT could help her with the painful periods she had been experiencing. This time, Laura composed her own set up statements. We used:

"Even though I suffer from really painful periods, I deeply and completely accept myself"

"I accept myself, even though my periods cripple me"

"Even though I get the cramps with my period, I deeply and completely accept myself"

"Even though periods are a total pain, I choose to embrace them with love"

I gave Laura a copy of the EFT procedure to take away with her, and told her to use it as a first aid tool if she started to feel pain at her next period.

A few weeks later I had a call from her. When her period was due she had started to get a cramp and had tapped it away. Every time she got the slightest twinge, she had tapped on it. She was now partway through her second virtually pain-free period since learning how to use EFT!

MARTHA
Knee pain

Martha's knee was very painful and I suggested applying EFT. It was an old injury which flared up from time to time so she didn't think a 'tapping session' would help much, but was prepared to try.

She scored her pain at a 9 and we used:

"Even though I have this pain in my knee I deeply and completely accept myself"

It went down to 7. We did a round for the 'remaining' pain and she said it was much worse, but now it was what she would describe as an ache rather than a pain.

We did two rounds on this ache and it disappeared.* Another 'one minute wonder'. She was very impressed with EFT, and I told her a bit about the history and how it had been originally designed to collapse negative emotions.

Some time later I spoke to Martha. She was having problems with a subordinate work colleague who was making life very difficult for her, and other staff. She told me that she had been tapping on this issue and found it really helped her to cope.

*Author's note: This shift, from pain to ache, demonstrates the importance of being specific in your set-up statements,

128

It was about a year later that I next spoke to Martha. I asked her if she was still using EFT in her everyday life. "Yes," she replied, "but I only use the points on my fingers now and it still works. Is that OK?" The joys of EFT! What a wonderful therapy this is!

Afterword

I wrote this book because I am passionate in my desire to raise awareness of the existence, and the healing power, of EFT. In chapter one I asked you to leave your belief systems behind for the time it took you to read this book because I wanted you to experience EFT for yourself with an open, curious mind.

Hopefully, if you have tried EFT on a simple issue, you will now have resolution of that issue. The chances are that specific issue will never be a problem again. You have experienced healing on a personal level and know that EFT works.

Try it on everything. You have nothing to lose but a few minutes of your time. For minor aches and pains it takes less time to stay where you are and do a round or two of EFT; than to get up, fetch a glass of water, find the paracetamol, take them and then wait half an hour or so for them to work.

If you are specific in your set up phrases and persistent in your efforts, you *will* get results.

Please use EFT wisely. You must take responsibility for your own physical, spiritual and emotional health and well being. If your emotional problems are overwhelming, you may find it easier at first to work with an experienced EFT practitioner.

Do not use it on any long standing or chronic illness without the knowledge of your GP, hospital consultant or other health practitioner.

If you need help or guidance, please feel free to e-mail me, ~~Jean@theEFTsite.co.uk~~ or you could enrol in a workshop to get some 'hands on' experience. Check your local paper for any workshops being held in your area.

If you have access to a personal computer, you could visit my website at ~~www.theEFTsite.co.uk~~ where you will find details of my own workshops. To find details of workshops in your area, click on the link to Gary Craig's 'official' website, where you will also find lists of practitioners as well as countless case histories, up to date research information and tutorials which are free to download.

Try EFT on everything - be specific in your set-up statements and be persistent. And when you get success....spread the word!

If you need help, contact me on JeanFaithful@aol.com

131

ADDENDUM

Since writing this book my colleague Isy Grigg and I have joined forces and formed a partnership, The Prometheus Partnership, to research the effectiveness of EFT in the treatment of PTSD, specifically for people who have suffered their original trauma in the line of duty; i.e. armed forces, rescue services etc.

Many of these men have been told that there is nothing more that can be done for them in mainstream medicine, other than learning coping strategy or using drug therapy. Some have been suffering from PTSD for decades and EFT can help them.

Our hypothesis is

"In six sessions, EFT will produce great reductions in self-reported symptoms of Post Traumatic Stress Disorder in participants who have tried other treatments which have as yet failed to bring about significant relief; and that these changes will be maintained over time."

Although this study is in its infancy, the results so far have been awesome. Here, in their own words, are the stories of two of our first participants.

Case Study 008

"I am a police officer of 14 years service. Until November 1998 I was a normal, 'happy with life' person, content in my job and a loving family. Early December, 1998, I attended a horrific murder scene, with the victim known to me. This would and still has changed my life. Three months later I became unwell. My first symptoms were being unable to sleep, anxiety and feeling depressed. I visited my G.P. who, on relaying the circumstances of the incident, diagnosed me as suffering from Post Traumatic Stress. My blood pressure was extremely high and I was immediately prescribed medication for this and also anti-depressants.

"I was then referred to my local Primary Mental Health Team. By now other symptoms of Post Traumatic Stress appeared, such as loss of sex drive, memory loss, mood swings, lethargy and I started to drink alcohol heavily. I felt I had become a mental and physical wreck. My concerns of harm to, or loss of life of, my family or how I would cope with it had become obsessive. I could not see any hope for the future at this time.

"I spent 12 months with the health team, attending once a fortnight. During this time and because my symptoms were still affecting myself and my family, my counsellor at the health team stated that my Post Traumatic Stress had become

Post Traumatic Stress **Disorder**. This was as far as the Health Team could help me.

"My blood pressure was still high and I was also put on a higher strength anti-depressant. I was referred to a specialist P.T.S.D. counsellor in Bristol where I spent a further 19 months having counselling sessions. During this time I was able to understand the physical and emotional problems I was suffering and during this time my symptoms became less severe.

"In March 2005 I met Jean Faithful & Isy Grigg for the start of six sessions of EFT. At that time I was still taking medication for my blood pressure, and sleeping tablets. I still suffered from insomnia, mood swings, anxiety, some mild depression and fears for my family. I also had numerous panic attacks which obviously caused embarrassment to my family and social life.

"The first session consisted of EFT being explained to me. I was uncertain at the beginning but was hopeful that EFT could help me improve my quality of life. Also during the first session we started using the treatment. This was done by getting me to recall the incident which caused the P.T.S.D. At certain points my emotion and stress levels would rise. Isy and Jean would then start several rounds of tapping on my meridian points until the emotion or negative thoughts subsided. After the first session I remember feeling exhausted and I slept very well.

"During the next 3 sessions we worked on recalling the incident, piece by piece. At one particularly distressing point I had a high level of anxiety in the back of my neck and head. *After 3 rounds of tapping I felt this pressure move and release itself through my nose. By now I could see that EFT was able to assist me by turning my negative thoughts into positive thoughts.

"I had now learnt to apply EFT to myself any time night or day whenever any negative thoughts occur. Isy and Jean also explained that EFT could be used, not only for P.T.S.D. but also for anything that causes emotional problems. By the time I had started my last session I noticed that the recalling or triggers associated with the incident had become less common and distressing. I was able to dismiss them easier and more quickly. I have learnt to look at the positive side of events or problems, rather than the negative side. My outlook for myself and my family is much more positive. I now have the tools of EFT to help me through any current problems and emotions and anything else that might crop up.

"As I stated at the beginning I was uncertain as to whether EFT would be able to help with PTSD but I am convinced it has helped me now and will in the future."

*Author's note: This anxiety manifested itself as intense tension and pressure

Case Study 010

"Dear Jean & Isy

"As requested I append below a statement on my wellbeing after attending your EFT sessions. I hope my remarks and comments will go someway to helping you in your quest to benefit all those unfortunate enough to suffer from PTSD for whatever reasons. I apologise for the delay in sending this to you.

"After the six sessions of EFT given by Jean and Isy, I feel much more confident in myself and I am also much happier. I do not now feel the need to go to my safe place, i.e. my garage and can deal with my anger and aggressiveness without any problems.

"Following the tapping techniques I have been taught to use I have even learnt how to control my aches and pains, all to good advantage. My rages are now controlled and, whilst driving, I feel comfortable and can dismiss any improprieties caused by other road users quite easily.

"I feel a lot more relaxed and I find I can deal with everyday problems now without becoming angry or threatened. By using EFT I can cope with most irritating or annoying occurrences which may arise and not lose my temper, especially with my wife as I did before, and which in turn is good for her also. If I should feel myself becoming stressed a round or two of EFT really does help.

"On the whole I was extremely impressed by the treatment given and the after-effects. Even after the initial session I noticed a vast improvement, feeling much calmer in myself, as though a huge mental and physical weight was being lifted off me. Associated with this was a physical sensation likened to a tight coil being unravelled in my stomach.*

"I would certainly recommend this technique to anyone who has similar problems to myself and I do extol the benefits I have experienced to as many people I meet as possible and hope it will help them as much as it has helped me. Thank you Jean & Isy, I hope your efforts are well rewarded.

Yours sincerely

(Not forgetting my wife)

*Author's note: When asked, our volunteer took a while to describe what was happening to him at this point. He said he felt that a tight coil had been removed from his stomach but could not describe what he felt now. He then realised that there was no feeling there **to** describe.. the pain, which he had felt for so long that it had become 'normal' to him, was gone! This tightness has not returned.

Both of these men received only six, one hour sessions of EFT spread over a period of six weeks. The progress they made was way beyond their expectations. Both had received many different therapies but nothing had 'cured' them. Drugs and strategies to help you to live with it seem to be the way the mainstream medical profession treats PTSD.

Luckily, some medical students are now being taught to look at the patient holistically; as an individual with different experiences and traumas in their lives that have made them the person they are, instead of just a bag full of bones and organs and systems which break down and need to be mended. This is good news indeed!

As I said before, EFT is in its infancy, but the word is spreading, thanks to its numerous success stories. Please, when you have *your* successes, spread the word. Try it on your family. Introduce it to your friends, neighbours and work colleagues.

The world needs EFT!